please take care of this book too

twelve steps home

by suzanne j. cairns & elizabeth j. saunders

First published in the United Kingdom in 2015 by
The Choir Press

ISBN 978-1-910864-10-4

I am whispering,
can you hear me ?

Are you near me,
can you feel me?

Please, take me,

home.

for all the topsys out there

Please take care of this book too.

acknowledgements

with thanks to:

the wordwitch, the fixer, the shapeshifter, the greenman, the shaker, the crimper,

the keyholder, the arranger, the needlewoman, the polisher, the interrogator & the

notegirl, without whom this book would not have been possible.

Special thanks to:

Gareth & Simon, Tim, Ewan, Donna, Tony, Sue, Charles, Steuart, Sarah, Stuart, Frank,

Wendy, Gill, & Dave, for their safe pairs of hands

the 12 steps

books undercover

- an author's note-

How often have you heard someone declare, "I should write a book ." The truth is that each and every one of us is a soup of syllables and experiences waiting to be read. If we are lucky the number of chapters lengthen as the years pass, and the plot lines merge and diverge, as we are ever hopeful of a happy ending.

Evidence of those who have committed their narratives to paper are everywhere. Tomes large and small, fat and thin, perch on shelves, windowsills and desks in an array of colours, bindings and languages. They prop open doors, educate, illuminate, decorate and irritate in equal measure. Like nets, they catch their author's thoughts and serve them, fresh from the heart on a platter, nectar to some whilst indigestible to others.

However, whether published or not, we are all looking for our stories to be read. Hoping for a gentle hand to turn our pages, hear our words and of course, never to judge us by our covers. Since time immemorial across the globe, humanity has yearned for its unique books to be taken care of. This is the simple tale of one more, a certain LGB.

sjc

the
wordwitch's
tale

stepping out and stepping up

There's a chink, a glint,
a sudden rush of fear,
a poke,
clutched hope
and a belly of confusion.

A choked breath lassos the scene, scavenging for comfort,
maybe there's a seam, between a nightmare and a dream,
a crisp wisp of blue that can transport me?
The muttering eyes of quizzical strangers,
sentries to this limestone manger –
a sacrifice to analyse,
a trophy or a joke,
a one stop shop for the cynical,
a beacon wrapped in a cloak . . .
of embarrassment?

There's a splinter
of magenta
as the night sky gulps the day,
a rudderless shudder
that engulfs me.

This is the tale of a very special little book; an account of its tortuous journey back to the safety and security from whence it had come. The story began at Malham Cove on an almost perfect Spring day, with hazy sunshine and a cloudless cobalt-blue sky which was gently caressed by a balmy breeze. Not a location where buckets and spades are in vogue, as the name infers, but a huge curving rock formation topped by a deeply eroded limestone pavement, dominating this part of the North Yorkshire landscape.

The clement weather, acting like a magnet, had drawn ramblers and climbers out in force, assembling to rest, admire the spectacular views or search the skies for a glimpse of the elusive peregrine falcons. Suddenly even the murmuring voices ceased and, in unison, the throng turned and stared as two men appeared as if by magic. Suited and booted in bona fide bodyguard apparel, with ear pieces and radios, their attention was fixed on a small brown paper parcel carried by the tallest and most imposing of them. Halting and ignoring the curious stares, the man gently drew out of the package what appeared to be a small green book, and placed it almost reverently, on an isolated rock. Having completed their task, without a word spoken, the pair about turned and calmly walked away. Bizarrely, the onlookers made no attempt to approach the object, and gathering their belongings together, they quietly drifted away. Something very special had obviously happened here.

As daylight began to fade, the tiny tome remained perched on the rock high above the valley, isolated and abandoned. The pervading silence broken only by the laughing call of the green woodpecker and the piercing screams of the swifts zooming overhead. In an instant however, this peaceful scene was rudely interrupted by a shrill warning cry from a little grey owl perched on a nearby hawthorn bush. Seconds later, a scruffy canine, of indeterminate breed, hurtled out of the gloom and came to a juddering halt in front of the book. Without pausing for breath, the dog grabbed the pages between sharp teeth, turned tail and shot off in the direction from which he'd come.

Meanwhile some distance away a roly-poly lady, coat flapping and lead dangling, could be seen trudging up the slope. She stopped every few moments to catch her breath and shout to her dog, who appeared to have vanished. Just as she was about to abandon her search, a ragged bundle of fur made a dramatic entrance and dropped a damp object at her feet. Standing back, tongue lolling, he waited expectantly for a positive reaction to this gift. He was therefore taken aback when his owner grabbed his collar, attached the lead, and berated him for his bad behaviour. After stuffing the item into her rucksack and with the dejected animal in tow, the woman stomped back down to the village as fast as her plump legs could carry her.

Arriving back home in a foul mood she sent the unhappy hound to bed, grabbed a glass of sweet sherry, and began to prepare for the school trip to Bolton Abbey. In the process of repacking her rucksack she pulled out and glanced through the little green book. She sighed her indifference to the contents and placed it to one side. She knew however, that a colleague had a passion for both poetry and photography, and that examples of both could be found within the covers of this small tome.

The following day, with the book back in its prison, surrounded by the walls and bars of a sandwich box, a flask, worksheets and the odd inhaler or two, the over-excited, chattering children, set off for Bolton Abbey. The harassed teacher, looked as if she'd rather be anywhere than with this particular class, who had the reputation for being the most demanding in school. The wordwitch, (she who should be obeyed), gathered the disparate band together, and with instructions to keep well away from the water's edge ringing in their ears, the motley crew moved off.

All appeared be to going smoothly as the troop made their way, in a lack-adaisical fashion, along the river bank. Suddenly there was a yell, as one of the boys slipped slowly but surely into the water. Rushing to the rescue the teacher grabbed the child, and in the undignified process of hauling him out, almost lost her rucksack to a watery grave. Meanwhile, during this foray the remainder of the group were having a wonderful time, laughing and joking and thoroughly enjoying the discomfiture of both teacher and pupil. With a face like thunder, she swung round and screamed like a banshee at the class. The bedraggled boy was next on the agenda. With eyes flashing she scathingly suggested he sort himself out. Turning to the soggy rucksack, she irritably tipped out the contents, gave a sigh of relief that the only damage was to the cover of the little book - and that really didn't matter after all!

With a final warning to tow the line or else, the rather subdued youngsters set off, clip-boards in hands. Before long, with natural exuberance restored, excited students could be seen scuttling hither and thither searching for answers to the questions they'd been set. This hive of activity continued until someone whispered the word 'food!!' With concentration lost the wordwitch decided to call a halt. Before you could say 'Jack Robinson', the whole shooting match could be seen making their way eagerly towards the cafe and picnic area, rushing to find seats, despite orders to the contrary. Calm descended as lunch boxes were opened and the predictable crisps and chocolate bars extracted. Within minutes the inevitable happened; a child began to wheeze and struggle for breath. Oh no, thought the wordwitch, an asthma attack; that's just about the last straw. Looking in total control, with no hint of her true feelings, she quickly found the right inhaler thus averting a possible tragedy. Drama over, lunch completed and with bags packed, the unruly class moved off to continue their day.

There was however a silent casualty, that had gone unnoticed during the lunchtime fracas. The little green book (LGB to its friends), was left forsaken, staring at the underside of the picnic table, its damp cover speckled with crisps and soggy cake crumbs. A sorry sight.

a strange affair

My coming out party was a strange affair,
sets of gleaming teeth and unkempt hair.
There were roller-coaster anecdotes, peppered with hilarity,
born on the lips of children, known for their polarity,
corralled by insincerity, inflexible temerity,
a peculiar, helter-skelter sort of do.

Yes, my coming out party was a strange affair,
shame that no-one noticed
that I was even there.

APB all wordsmiths –
'WANTED – A NOM DU GUERRE!'

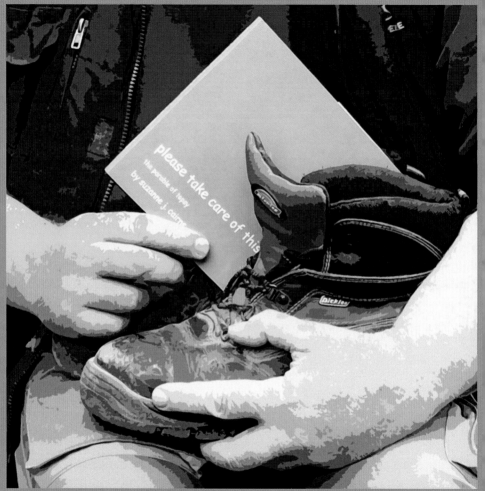

please take care of this

the parable of ready

by suzanne j. cairns

the
fixer's
tale

undercover

My virgin spine is flexing now,

we're going undercover,

these calloused hands

my rescuer,

my fantasy,

my lover.

I quiver, tremble, shiver,

stumble, stutter, flutter,

this glory unfamiliar,

from my exile in the gutter.

I tango on your lips,

the servant of your touch,

I never thought that I would take to

lap dancing this much.

A diminutive flock of sparrows stood like soldiers on parade, chests puffed out, spindly legs akimbo, preparing to attack the tasty morsels lying beneath the picnic table. They waited patiently, like statues, whilst a sour-faced woman trudged past, followed by a crocodile of boisterous, vociferous children. With the enemy in retreat, their planned assault was abruptly thwarted, by the untimely arrival of a laughing gang of men. With wings flapping, indicating their displeasure and frustration, the band conceded defeat.

The group dressed in working garb, tattoos proudly on display, ambled towards the picnic area oblivious to the distress they'd caused the feathered troop. With much clattering and banging, seats were found and the youngest member of the crew despatched to order refreshments. Eventually, with steaming cups of tea, a plate piled high with sticky buns and fags lit, the men sat companionably enjoying a well deserved break. Conversation, as you can imagine, dominated by football!

What of the little book? As the heated debate continued above, sticky crumbs, ash and cigarette stubs were accumulating on its once pristine cover. However, just as LGB was on the verge of disappearing beneath this unsavoury, smelly pile of debris, a large weather-beaten hand materialised. Surreptitiously, the book was grasped and slipped unobtrusively into a deep pocket. The men, heedless of the drama beneath their feet, reluctantly drew the conversation to an end. With the last drops of tea consumed, en masse and with some reluctance, the group departed to resume their labours. It would be several hours before the little book saw daylight again.

The fixer, feeling bone tired and grimy, arrived home later than expected. A long, hot, luxurious shower, followed by a scrumptious steak and kidney pie, did much to restore his equilibrium. Pouring out a thirst-quenching Lowenbrau, he fished out the book purloined earlier, and with a deep sigh, settled down to explore the contents. Within minutes he was drawn into an imaginary world of picture and verse, the beer, gradually losing its frothy head, forgotten. Time slipped by and at last, with great reluctance, the fixer placed the book to one side and made his weary way to bed. Not to the peaceful night he'd envisaged, but to one peppered with dreams that made little or no sense.

In one scene he found himself deep in a dark gloomy forest surrounded by trees with gnarled trunks, branches like wizened arms and leaves that resembled cadaverous fingers. This nightmarish scene was further compounded by the presence of hundreds of books of every conceivable shape and size, hanging precariously balanced above the forest floor. As this picture began to fade the image was replaced with an equally bizarre one. In this instance miniature books, with legs encased in wellingtons and covers protected by matching raincoats, played. Chattering and with squeals of laughter they cavorted, like happy children, at the base of a cascading waterfall. The fixer, woken abruptly by the persistent harsh ringing of an alarm clock, turned over and attempted to finish his dream. He was eager to discover more about these tiny tomes. A pointless exercise! Feeling jaded and with a sense of total unreality he hauled himself out of bed. The day ahead back at Bolton Abbey had little appeal!

Late morning, with repairs to a dry stone wall complete, the fixer was more than ready to down tools and take an early break. With the Rare Book Shop closed for lunch, he found a secluded table and settled down to enjoy a Cornish pasty he'd bought, and the book he'd rescued. Abruptly this tranquil scene was interrupted by the roar of an approaching car. A beautiful red convertible swung into sight driven by a stunning blonde. As the fixer gulped down the last mouthful of his snack, almost choking in the process, an exquisite woman gracefully emerged. With jaw dropping and eyes on stalks he stared in disbelief. This surely couldn't be the actress he'd always admired? Never for a moment had he expected to catch a glimpse of her in real life. LGB forgotten, and as if turned to stone, he watched in amazement as this mesmeric woman appeared to glide serenely towards him. Halting, she quite charmingly asked if she could sit down. Lost for words, the fixer merely nodded a response. Used to this reaction from the public at large, this charismatic star swiftly lightened the atmosphere. Soon the pair could be seen chatting like old friends.

Enjoying every moment of this encounter the man was brought back to earth, with a thud, when the door of the book shop opened. He looked at his watch aghast, he had no idea it was so late. With a hasty farewell he rushed back to his van, jumped in and shot off, disappearing in a cloud of dust. The little green book he was supposed to care about was completely overlooked. Fortunately all was not lost, the actress glancing down caught sight of LGB. Carefully she scooped it up and gently tucked it into the depths of her soft leather bag. A safe refuge, perhaps?

gone

Like a feather touching crystal
you
eased me into your song,
tip-toed through my rhythms
and then,
in a flash,

you
were

gone.

the shapeshifter's tale

prickled

Prickled by passing flattery,

bewildered, dazed and confused,

I'm perching on a pedestal,

another suitor's muse?

Dazzled by this spotlight,

you're hinged on my every word,

stroking as you turn me,

it's suspiciously absurd.

But,

a geisha to the glory, you allure me to your story and

my words begin to trickle down your veins.

I'm tempted,

it's authentic?

Or

am I just a victim of my dreams?

A flaky, shaky, creature of extremes?

Mission accomplished at the Rare Book Shop, the shapeshifter carefully tucked a small brown package, together with her bag, safely into the well of the car. She meandered home along little used roads at a leisurely pace, soaking up the peaceful ambience of the countryside. Not a soul in sight, a far cry from the hustle and bustle of London, from which she'd briefly escaped. With every mile signs of human habitation decreased, with isolated farms the norm. The actress finally drew the car to a halt outside a tiny stone-built cottage, which nestled into the surrounding hillside. Her bolt-hole, much needed after weeks of performing, night after night, in a particularly challenging role.

London and the stage were the last thoughts on her mind as she carried the parcel inside. She hoped the contents, on closer examination, would live up to expectations. Brown paper removed, an exquisite miniature of The Tempest was revealed, the cover fine Moroccan leather and the title gold-embossed. On closer inspection this tiny treasure was perfect, with no sign of foxing or spots to spoil the gilt-edged pages. The actress was thrilled, a perfect addition to her collection; but more of that later. Her thoughts turned to the little green book which remained in the depths of the bag. What hidden delights might be found were a mystery the shapeshifter was determined to resolve, as soon as time allowed. A hectic afternoon followed, but finally with e-mails answered and phone calls made, it was time for a spot of literary detective work. Self indulgence too perhaps!

Showered, shampooed and dressed in a cosy onesie, with chilled wine to hand, the actress was ready for action! The first item on the agenda was a large wooden box. As the lid slowly opened a colourful world of miniature books was revealed, part of a vast collection of tiny tomes the shapeshifter had acquired over many years. Some were encased in leather of various hues, others bound in marbled board, whilst a few had covers made from mottled tortoiseshell, delicate mother of pearl and even ivory. Their titles and genres were equally diverse. With a smile, the actress gently added the latest member of the family to the mix and turned her attention to the little green book.

Wine glass refreshed the shapeshifter picked up LGB. The title, an unusual one, fascinated her. Surely most people took care of books? With this question unanswered she turned to the first poem and began to read aloud, bringing the words alive as she spoke. A performance sadly with no audience present. The rendition of the first section complete the actress gently closed the tome. This was something special, something to be savoured, not rushed. Relaxed and at peace with the world the shapeshifter drifted off to bed, to sleep and to dream.

Images of books of various shapes, sizes and colours, drifted through her subconscious mind. As the witching hour approached the scene slowly changed as they gained a momentum of their own. Twisting and twirling they began to rotate, gathering speed to form a kaleidoscope of convoluted patterns and hues. This whirlpool of activity then stopped as abruptly as it had begun. As the image began to fade all that remained was a barely perceptible patchwork design with a tiny green tome at the centre. The actress woke with a start, something had threatened her beloved books. She leapt out of bed and ran downstairs, only to find LGB and the miniatures exactly as they'd been left, safe, secure and undamaged. With a sigh of relief that no harm had been done, it was time to put fanciful thoughts to one side and get on with the day.

A while later, a chauffeur driven limousine arrived at the race track and drew up at the members enclosure. As the rear door opened a dazzling woman calmly stepped out, a picture of elegance personified. Heads turned as this stunning creature, dressed in a striking aquamarine outfit, paused, thanked the driver, then slowly moved on. Quite an entrance by the actress! A glass or two of champagne later, the shapeshifter felt completely relaxed and decided on a whim to go down to the track. A decision she would live to regret. Bag on shoulder, with the little green book safely inside, she began to ease her way through the throng. Soon the actress was swept up by the atmosphere and the excitement of the vociferous crowd who cheered and shouted as the horses thundered by. So engrossed, she was oblivious to an unsavoury, down at heel individual who watched her every move as he silently inched his way forward. Closing in, like a lion stalking its prey, the crook pounced, grabbed the shapeshifter's bag and melted away into the vast sea of people.

With the bag tucked under his tatty coat the thief strolled nonchalantly on, gradually leaving the hordes behind. He found an isolated spot and eager to examine his loot, the heister tipped out the contents of the bag. Rooting through the haul he quickly repacked those items of value and discarded those, in his eyes, which had no monetary worth. Swag tucked securely back in the confines of his voluminous coat, this weasel of a man scuttled off. The only evidence of his presence was a lipstick, a few tissues and a little green tome. A sorry state of affairs. BUT, out of nowhere, a pair of familiar, comforting hands enclosed the book, dusted it down and placed it gently on a nearby fence.

Picking through the promises
trapped between my teeth,
hope is that subtle life raft,
that tugs and then retreats.
A castaway on your memory,
a flounder amongst this trash,
slapped by the waves of emptiness,
my pitted breath
calling you back.

the greenman's tale

capiche ?

I need to find my niche.
Capiche?

Corrugated me
flexing to another's puny reed, weeding through
these characters,
these demands,
these empty seeds.
Bugger the eye of the needle
and prancing on this pin.

I need to find my niche.
Capiche?

The last race run, the crowds began their mass exodus home, thoughts of success and failure on hold, whilst they pushed and shoved eager to reach the open road. As the last trailer trundled off into the distance, weary horses safely ensconced, a swarthy figure emerged from a barely perceptible gap in the hedge, and nonchalantly strolled towards the fence. Reaching his goal the man casually gathered up the objects he'd spied earlier; a green book and a very expensive lipstick. Slipping the booty into a pocket the greenman turned tail and crept quietly away. He disappeared into the woodland beyond, where his faithful dog patiently waited.

The pair moved silently through the trees, along a little used path, impatient to reach the sanctuary of home. Veering off the track, the greenman pushed his way through the undergrowth, pausing momentarily to survey the timeless scene that confronted him. In pride of place in this fairy tale glade, and surrounded by a profusion of wild flowers, stood a beautiful gypsy caravan. Ornately painted in crimson, with elaborate carvings of birds and flowers picked out in shades of green and yellow, it was a sight to behold. Grazing close by a traditional gypsy cob, black and white in colour, sensed its masters' presence and lifting a noble head, whinnied a gentle greeting. With spell broken, the greenman moved purposefully forward, swinging the door of the van open to reveal an interior steeped in history. At the far end stood a cast-iron stove, on which a pan gently simmered, to the right, a built in berth and opposite in pride of place, a glass-fronted cabinet. Moving quickly and efficiently in this familiar space, the hungry animals were soon fed and chores completed.

With a campfire lit, the greenman settled down to examine the goods he'd acquired. First the lipstick came under scrutiny. It was obviously expensive and on closer inspection, brand new, something his daughter would appreciate perhaps? Next he turned his attention to the little green book. Opening the cover he meticulously worked his way from front to back, looking for any sign of damage. With none apparent, apart from a tiny mark possibly caused by damp, he resolutely snapped it shut. Another potential candidate for the book shop at Stow, he thought. Re-entering the van, the lipstick was tucked into a drawer containing an eclectic assortment of items, whilst LGB was assigned to a much deeper one, full of books of every conceivable shape, size and colour. A gloomy prison with no obvious date for release.

As the day drew to a close the glade took on an almost ethereal quality, with the only light from the moon and the dancing flames of the fire. The greenman picked up his flute and began to play, slowly and gently at first, with the soft whispering notes wafting into the night beyond. As the music continued, the sound gained an almost unearthly, haunting quality, soothing the audience as they gradually appeared. The first to slip quietly into the auditorium was a red fox with tiny cubs at heel, followed closely by the stately entrance of a magnificent badger. Finally, a fallow deer tip-toed tentatively through the undergrowth and cautiously approached the arena. Silently they lay down side by side, mesmerised by the brilliance and dream-like quality of the music. A short time later a pair of rabbits, a hedgehog and a squirrel soundlessly joined the group. The greenman played on and on until the moon disappeared behind a cloud, and the fire was nothing more than a few glowing embers. As the music began to fade the creatures, with the most vulnerable first, began to drift quietly away. A spell-binding interlude.

By contrast as dawn broke, the glade was a hive of activity as the greenman prepared to leave for the long trek south. With goods stowed, the horse harnessed and the dog barking with excitement, the trio set off. They'd be back, God willing, within the year.

As the weeks passed, the entourage made slow but steady progress towards Stow. Eventually reaching the outskirts momentum slowed to almost a snails pace, as caravans of every conceivable shape and size converged on the picturesque town. The customary calm replaced by a frenzy of activity and a cacophony of sounds. Dogs barked frantically as they rushed about wildly, narrowly avoiding the ever-present wheels of both cars and vans. Horses whinnied anxiously, whilst the human contingent competed with one another to be heard above the din. This chaos and confusion was further compounded, by the unexpected arrival of a youth, recklessly driving a skinny black and white pony straight towards a gaily-painted horse-drawn van. The greenman sat transfixed, gazing in horror as the duo approached. As they swept by with barely an inch to spare, his gasp of relief was instantly followed by a furious torrent of words, totally wasted on the feckless boy. Soothing the petrified horse and calming the alarmed dog, he picked up the reins for the final leg of their lengthy and exhausting journey.

The following morning after a good nights sleep, the greenman woke refreshed. He had one task to complete before he could relax and enjoy the delights of the fair. Moving purposefully towards an ornate chest, he slowly pulled open the deep drawer at the base. Rays of light percolated the gloomy interior, revealing the arsenal of books for the first time in weeks. To avoid mishap, the greenman removed the tomes one by one placing them carefully in a pile. LGB, finally released from its somber tomb, held prime position on top. Gathering the bundle together and with faithful hound in tow, the duo set of purposefully towards the centre of Stow. Approaching the High Street his attention was caught by the sight of a familiar figure in the distance.

An elderly lady was striding briskly down the hill, an old friend of many years standing. They shared a common interest in fighting for the rights of travellers, and both felt the traditions of the horse fair should be maintained. With a final spurt, the pair converged on the bookshop and entered together, one to sell, the other to buy. Distracted, the greenman casually placed his wares on the counter, but in a matter of seconds they began to slide swiftly out of control. The woman lurched forward, frantically grabbing at the unwieldy pile as it hurtled through space. With a crash, they landed and scattered across the hard wooden floor. There was one sole survivor of this failed rescue attempt. LGB was now held tightly in the hands of the shaker. Their fate together was sealed and clutching the tiny tome to her ample bosom, she made a swift purchase. The little green book was safe at last!

crooks and nannies

weary,

d r e a r y,

t
e
a
r

y   and

lost,

foxed by the
ambulance chasers,
two facers, empty pacers
whose only concern is cost.

Among these ingle-crooks and nannies,
where barbs are taunting birds,
surely there's a prophet who will understand my words?

the shaker's tale

pachyderm

Today,
I shall be largely a pachyderm.
I know it sounds preposterous,
but I've decided to align with
the hippo
and
rhinoceros.
Thick-skinned, heavy-limbed,
armoured, primed for battle,
allergic to your sob-stories and puny tittle-tattle.
I'll frown, pound, undermine,
I'll revel in your fear,
the fleeter cheetah's dextrous metre,
mown into second gear.

but,
who's this tumble-weeding soul,
so soft and disinclined
this hapless, wretched, empty, beast –
Oops . . . I'm feeling
kind!

The next day found the elderly lady smartly dressed in her best tweed suit, highly polished shoes and, incongruously, a rather battered hat, sitting on a crowded train hot-foot for London. On the table in front of her were a pile of papers which appeared to contain lists of signatures, and a much slimmer document. Picking up the latter she began to read. This was the report she'd compiled, hoping to persuade 'the powers that be' that the horse fair should remain on its current site. She was a historian by trade and found the background and development of the fair fascinating. Apparently there had been markets at Stow for centuries, but in 1476 Edward IV decreed a fair should be held biannually, on set dates, to encourage trade within the town. As the years passed these grew in size and importance, with Stow prospering as a result. However, with an increase in vandalism and crime many felt the time had come for the fair to be relocated. Others believed that, with additional policing and street cleaners, the tradition could be maintained, a view firmly held by the shaker. Report checked, the papers were gathered together and placed in her satchel as she drew out the little green book.

The shaker, a traditionalist, loved real books and couldn't imagine ever owning an electronic device with no pages to turn! Ordering a coffee, she settled down to read. The background of the author and how the book came to be written intrigued her, delving more deeply, she was soon immersed in both pictures and verse. She loved the poems and the ideas reflected in each, and felt the images captured the essence of the words perfectly. Totally unaware of passing time, the shaker was brought back to earth with a bump, as the train slid noisily into Paddington station. Feeling flustered, she grabbed her barbour coat, thrust the little green book into the depths of the inside pocket, and with satchel in tow clambered off the train. She paused to catch her breath, before joining the seething mass of humanity, purposefully shoving their way towards the exit and the world beyond.

The shaker's next appearance was outside Downing Street and with petition delivered, the fate of the fair was now in the lap of the Gods (and the politicians). She had done her bit! The sun was shining as she slowly strolled away, relishing the thought of time spent as a tourist rather than a campaigner. A pleasant few hours followed ambling through the city, enjoying the various sights on offer. She even slipped into the Tate to see an exhibition recommended by a friend, but it made no sense to her at all! Approaching Trafalgar Square, the shaker became aware of a strange roaring sound above the noise of the traffic. Turning a corner, a scene of total mayhem confronted her. A large angry throng were screaming and shouting whilst police, in riot gear, brandished batons and tried to restore order. In seconds, the elderly woman was swallowed up and swept along by the mob. Terrified and hanging on to her satchel and coat for dear life, she was pushed and shoved by the inflamed masses. Expecting to be trampled to death at any moment, the shaker tried desperately to maintain her balance. Inch by inch she eased her way towards the edge of the crowd. Glancing up and noting the presence of a salon of some kind, she made a lunge for the door and safety. Tragically, in this final bid for freedom, the shaker collided with a burly youth and collapsed in a heap.

The door to the salon swiftly opened and a petite figure hurried out. Noting that the elderly woman was bleeding profusely from a head wound and appeared disorientated, the young girl quickly called for support. As the situation on the street remained turbulent, the shaker was gently ushered inside to wait for help to arrive. Within a short period of time, she found herself in the secure confines of an ambulance with the satchel thrust into her hands, just as the doors were closing. Without further ado, sirens blaring and blue lights flashing, the vehicle sped off. This was not how the day should have ended at all! As for LGB? It remained undiscovered, tucked securely in a very deep pocket inside a well worn barbour.

Daring to dream can be a hanging offence,
you tie yourself in nots
and before you know what's what,
you're short
of breath.

please take care of this book   by suzanne j. cairns

the crimper's tale

moving

I need to be held,
but are these
the right hands?
I long to be touched
but do we have
the same plans?

Can we share a dream,
can you read my mind?
Will you take me home?
Are you kind?

I need to be held
but are these
safe hands?
I long to be moved,
but are you a Don Juan,
simply moving me,

on?

As the ambulance disappeared from view, business within the salon soon reverted to normal. Foils were checked, rinses complete, whilst scissors snipped merrily away. This hive of activity continued until the last client, hair beautifully coiffured, drifted out into the city beyond. It had been a long and tiring day but, with a final burst of energy the salon was quickly spruced up and, with a cheery wave to their boss, the band of young stylists headed off, eager to get home.

The shop was eerily quiet, something the crimper relished after the perpetual buzz of noise throughout the day. She'd remained behind to cash up and get ready for what should be a very special evening. It was exactly one year to the day when the crimper met the love of her life. To celebrate this memorable event they'd booked a table at a top London restaurant, something they could ill afford! In a dress of dusky pink, with make-up re-done and hair immaculate, the crimper was, unusually, ready and waiting with time to spare.

Glancing round, her gaze fell upon a solitary coat, which someone had obviously left. With a sudden flashback, she visualised the woman who'd been rushed to hospital. Wondering if the pockets might hold a clue to her identity, the crimper gingerly thrust her hand into the depths of each. The outer ones were empty but the inside one held a small object that felt smooth and hard. Removing the item carefully from its hiding place, a little green book was revealed. Intrigued the crimper flipped slowly through the pages, pausing to examine the pictures which she loved. However, the poems were far more of a challenge, what did they mean? Her thoughts were rudely interrupted by a loud knocking at the door. Her date had arrived. Smiling at the face peering through the window, she gathered her bits and pieces together, including the little book, which she intended to read on the journey to Brighton the following day.

An hour later found the young lovers sipping champagne and soaking up the ambience of their very grand surroundings. Catching up on the events of their respective days, the crimper began to recount the tale of the unfortunate woman who had literally landed on the doorstep of the salon, and the book that had been left behind. Just as she withdrew the little tome from its resting place the waiter arrived with a mouth-watering platter of sea food. LGB could wait!!! The little book, was actually quite content, lying on a pristine white cloth, surrounded by sparkling silver, gleaming crystal and sweet smelling flowers. It was a much better place to be than the claustrophobic confines of a bag or pocket!

The young couple, totally engrossed in each other and chatting idly as they waited for the next course to arrive, were unaware of the gradual hush that descended on the room. Finally, alerted by the change in atmosphere, they glanced up; a beautiful woman escorted by an elegantly dressed man had just arrived. Instantly recognisable for the roles she'd played both on screen and stage, it was the shapeshifter, enjoying a rare evening out on the town. The youngsters, with eyes on stalks, watched as the actress strolled leisurely through the room. As she reached their table, she glanced down, stopped abruptly and without preamble picked up the little green book. "Could we join you for a moment?" she asked. Before the crimper could catch her breath, let alone answer, chairs had mysteriously appeared and more champagne ordered. The shapeshifter, apologising for their intrusion, explained that she was intrigued by the presence of the book. As far as she knew only one copy existed and that had been stolen at the racecourse in York.

What followed was an evening the young couple would never forget. They found themselves dinning with the shapeshifter, swapping stories about the little green book and theorising about its reappearance in London. Where had it been, what had happened since the theft and more to the point how was the elderly woman involved? Questions which would remain a mystery to all but LGB. The conversation gradually drifted to one of a more personal nature, as the actress was keen to discover more about the latest custodians of the book. As always, life is full of coincidences and it transpired that the shapeshifter's companion, a well known hotelier, was off to Brighton the following day. Within minutes the crimper, in a complete daze, found herself agreeing to the offer of a lift. Finally with arrangements made for the trip, and the actress insisting that the little tome could be returned at a later date, the young couple got up to leave. Glancing sheepishly at each other, in unison, they tentatively asked the shapeshifter for her autograph. Picking up the book and opening the front cover, she wrote… *This Book Is Special, Please Take Care Of It* … followed by a signature. LGB felt very proud!

pumped

Check out this slinky fox
throwing down some moves,
pumped, poised, self possessed,
unflappable and cool!
Easy does it tiger,
we know what you've been through,
but,
be mindful of the damage
a stray compliment can do.
Savour this excitement,
taste it to the core,
but remember the hands
that cradled you,
when you were on the floor.

please take care of this book

by suzo

care of this book

the keyholder's tale

trust

1000 and 1,
1000 and 2,
1000 and 3,
check.
Is it square?
Is it straight
or will I break my neck?
Knees together,
feet together,
toggle down to crutch,
drifting onto your drop zone,
flown in by your touch.
1000 and 1,
1000 and 2,
1000 and 3,
trust.
Do you care?
Is this love,
or a simple case of lust?

As one would expect the journey the following day went smoothly and according to plan. Much to the delight of the crimper her 'lift' arrived driving a top of the range Porsche, if only her friends could see her now, she thought, as she sank back into the soft leather seats. The powerful car ate up the miles and conversation moved inevitably to the subject of the little green book. The crimper explained that she'd spent some time reading the poems but admitted, rather sheepishly, that they didn't make a lot of sense. On impulse, the young woman turned to her companion, "I think this little tome is wasted on me, don't you? Take it and see what you think".

So here I am with yet another keeper, wondering what on earth the future holds. My relatively short life has certainly been a turbulent one. What I don't understand is why my author sent me away in the first place? I thought I was safe with her, but she arranged for two men to leave me on an isolated rock miles from anywhere, abandoned to my fate. There must have been a very good reason for her actions, because I know she loved me I am part of her after all. I prevaricate, what a long word for a little book like me, the sort of word used by the wordwitch. She was a miserable woman, who didn't care for me at all, she dunked me in the river and finally left me to rot beneath a table! Now I'm in Brighton in yet another bag, but a soft leather one this time, with a passport for company, waiting to see what happens next.

The keyholder and I were soon on the road again and the next time I saw daylight was for a brief moment, when the passport was taken out inspected and returned. Shortly afterwards a tannoy announced that a flight to Dubai was ready for boarding. From the reaction of my guardian that was obviously our destination. Little did I know that we'd be staying in one of the world's most luxurious hotels, in one of their most expensive suites. Journey complete I was released from the confines of the bag and placed on a magnificent, and very ornate, bedside table. There I remained in splendid isolation until finally, the elegant gentleman climbed into bed. He gently picked me up and slowly and carefully began to read the first poem, much nicer than flicking aimlessly through my pages. Verse complete, I was returned to my table and the light switched off, It had been a very long time since we had left Brighton! During the course of the next few days, life settled into a comfortable routine. I was left alone during the day, apart from the regular dusting I received, but spent the final moments of each night with the gentleman before he slept. On the fifth evening of our stay, the keyholder received an unexpected phone call, explaining that his trip to

Hong Kong had been brought forward, and we'd be leaving on an early morning flight. With packing a priority, our customary reading session didn't take place that night and back into the bag I went. I couldn't believe I was off on yet another trip, when would this stop? I just wanted to go home.

At yet another luxurious, but this time contemporary, hotel I was placed on a rather different bedside table, this one not at all to my liking. Expensive and stylish it might have been, but its cold and slippery surface was not designed with the safety of a book like me in mind. Again I was read each night and left each day until finally, one morning, I found that I was to be included in an excursion to see Big Buddha, whatever that was? Apparently it would involve a ferry trip to Lantau Island, a short journey by bus and finally a ride in a cable car, all very intriguing. Setting off on our adventure, I became increasingly aware of the humidity. It was so hot and clammy, surely I wouldn't survive in these conditions? What if my pages stuck together and I was irreparably damaged?

My anxiety increased when we reached the monastery and stopped for a well-earned rest. I could appreciate why the keyholder had chosen this particular spot. It was so peaceful amongst the almost tropical greenery with the smell of incense permeating the air, but why place me on a sticky damp table? Oblivious to my concerns, my guardian sat relaxing in the shade sipping an ice-cold drink. Without warning, the invasive ring of a mobile destroyed the tranquility of the scene. From what I could gather there were major problems at a hotel in Paris and the keyholder was required there post haste. He was to go directly to the airport, collect his luggage and catch an overnight flight. With a huge sigh my guardian reluctantly picked me up. I was sure neither of us relished the thought of another lengthy trip.

The little green book, with spirits flagging, was desperate to reach the safe haven it craved. If only LGB had known the journey was more than half-way through, what was to follow would have been much easier to bear.

prickles

Seeds were sewn in my pockets,

the day that I was born,

but now that they're fully fledged feelings,

their comfort has practically gone.

Someone has hidden my manual,

that explains how these growing pains work,

'cos maturity's no security,

when emotions are going berserk.

So, where do I turn for assistance,

down which path

is it safe

to be led?

Would somebody please explain

how to,

turn these prickles into petals in my head?

please take care of this bo[x]

the scraps of Reply

by Lawrence J. Currie

the arranger's tale

kindness

What does kindness smell of,

does it have a taste,

if I listen will I hear it,

can I see it in your face?

In the business lounge at the airport the keyholder sat relaxing, sipping a long cool gin and tonic, and reading the final poem contained within the cover of the little green book. Totally engrossed and in a world of his own, he was unaware that someone was trying to gain his attention, until a polite cough finally percolated his thoughts. Glancing up, he noted that a raven-haired woman was speaking, asking if she could share his table as all the others were full. Being a perfect gentleman, as etiquette demanded, he stood pulled out a chair and insisted that she join him for a drink. Needless to say this was the beginning of a very pleasant interlude for them both!

Before long, with the aid of the odd cocktail or two, the couple were completely relaxed and at ease. The keyholder discovered that the woman was on her own after a very distressing and messy divorce. She'd come to Hong Kong to visit friends and make some decisions about the future. Apparently this objective had been achieved, and she was now hot-foot back to England to begin the process of buying a flower shop and training to be a florist. The arranger went on to explain that she'd enrolled for a course in London, which covered both the business and creative aspects of her new career. What she really wanted to do was to concentrate on a contemporary approach when working with flowers, using natural materials to produce works of art. She began to chuckle at how pretentious she sounded, explaining that she would probably make a complete fool of herself. However, she had been reassured that no experience was necessary, just a willingness to get involved.

The keyholder intrigued by her story and aspirations, picked up the little book on impulse and suggested it might be something she'd enjoy. He pointed out that the photographs were beautiful and that the poems and philosophy behind the book were thought provoking. Furthermore it was time the little tome was passed on, explaining what he knew of its history. LGB was horrified by this announcement, yet another owner, with some fairly strange ideas about artistry and flowers to boot! Shortly after this change of ownership, the tannoy announced that the flight for London was ready for boarding. With a hasty farewell, and a promise to keep in touch, the pair went their separate ways - the arranger to London and the keyholder to Paris.

The woman had every intention of reading the little tome during the flight but, after the emotional toll of the last few days and the alcohol consumed, the arranger was soon fast asleep; dreaming of cities with buildings constructed, not from brick, but flowers of every imaginable hue. Waking as the aircraft approached London you can imagine her disappointment, when the city beneath her appeared dark, gloomy and austere, with not a flower in sight! As the plane landed and with all the activity that ensued the arranger quickly shook off her discomfiture, she was well rested and had much to look forward to. On a whim, and a phone call later, she had arranged to spend a few days in Dartmouth rather than go straight home. Another long trip for LGB.

Soon the arranger was safely ensconced on a coach bound for Paignton. She would then travel by steam train to Kingswear and finally catch the ferry across to Dartmouth, the former an experience she'd always dreamt about. With time to kill and no distractions, this was an ideal opportunity to begin reading the little book, the arranger thought. As the miles sped by she became more and more fascinated by its contents, intrigued by the messages within the poems. She reflected on the disastrous end to her relationship and wondered whether she could have handled the situation differently. Her musings were brought to an abrupt halt as the coach trundled into the bus station. Disembarking, she spent a few moments rearranging her luggage, ready for the next leg of the trip. The little book at this point was feeling rather squashed, rammed into the top of an already bulging holdall. A potential hazard for its rather frail cover!

Fortunately as the station was just a short stroll away, the arranger had time to purchase her ticket and a book outlining the history of the railway, from its conception, decline and restoration in the 1970's. Forcing this tome into the holdall and compressing LGB even further, she made her way onto the platform, just as the mighty Hercules steamed into view. What a magnificent sight it was too, it was difficult to imagine this gleaming monster, painted in Great Western Railway livery, was almost one hundred years old. Climbing aboard the pullman observation saloon, originally built for the Devon Belle service, the arranger gasped in delight. This was a real trip into the past and from this particular carriage she would have a unique view of the countryside. With curiosity aroused, the arranger removed the guide she'd bought, eager to learn more about this historic line. At that precise moment a piercing whistle and an answering bellow from Hercules, suggested the adventure was about to start. The arranger had no intention of missing a moment of the journey and put the book to one side, as the fiery beast set off.

Hercules huffing and puffing, with wheels clattering, made his way along the picturesque line. The arranger was enthralled by the breathtaking scenery as the mighty train made its way past colourful beach huts, through quaint stations, across viaducts, through tunnels and the dense woodland bordering the Dart Estuary. She hoped to spot some of the wildlife that made its home in this diverse landscape. Apparently, if you were lucky, you could catch sight of species such as buzzards, pheasants, herons, egrets and kingfishers, even dolphins and seals. All of this to be found along a track of a mere seven miles, quite amazing, the arranger thought. At this point, Hercules, with a final ear splitting blast, announced their arrival at Kingswear station.

Before long, the arranger was seated on the passenger ferry, making its way towards the picturesque town of Dartmouth. Her journey was almost at an end. Still clutching the guide book, she opened the holdall to tuck it away and glancing inside, she noticed 'something' was missing. Scrabbling through the contents, she searched in vain but the little green book had vanished! Where could it possibly be and more to the point, what could she do to find it? She had been entrusted to take care of the little tome and had failed totally !

full stop

If I was a punctuation mark,

I'd be a full stop.

Decisive. Robust. Rounded and compact.

There's no hanging around for a comma, as its tail slows up the plot

or stalling with a colon: semi or not.

Speech marks are a collusion of someone looking back,

inverted commas, clearly, a claustrophobic trap.

No need for the flare, devil-may-care, or extra hair,

of an exclamation mark!

An ampersand may be sexy (brackets a hint of something extra),

but we all know that a slash is largely crass.

@ is far too modern,

a question mark, plainly too unsure,

but a full stop is your friend

when you just,

can't take,

any more.

All these words inside me may be queueing up in line,
but the power of punctuation is undoubtedly divine.
If I could control yours –
my life would be . . .
deliciously,
sublime.

the needlewoman's tale

dig deep

You know in the depths of Winter,

when you think the sun has died

and the roofs hang onto the icicles,

that the broken hearted have cried?

Find the echoes of love

that grew you in the sun

and climb up that magical ladder that's

in each

and

every one

of us.

The little book meanwhile, was still on the train, having inadvertently fallen from the holdall and slipped down between the old plush seats. LGB was reasonably comfortable but bored, tired of travelling backwards and forwards between Paignton and Kingswear, listening to the same old comments from the passengers about the beautiful scenery and wildlife. If this goes on much longer, the little tome thought, I might do better in life as a tour guide rather than as a poetry book! As if in answer to a prayer a young lady, probably in her mid-twenties, sat down in the seat vacated by the arranger a few hours earlier. A pleasant change from some of the preceding occupants, mused LGB. One very large, rotund man sprang to mind; he'd almost buried the little book forever when he'd eased his bulky frame onto the seat.

The young woman, scanning the carriage with interest, glanced down and caught sight of something shiny protruding from the opulent, upholstered bench. Very gently, she placed her slender fingers into the cramped space and taking great care, she gradually eased the object towards the surface. With a pop, like a cork from a bottle, LGB tumbled out into the daylight; at the precise moment that Hercules pulled in at the station and the passengers began to disembark. The needlewoman, without a second thought, swiftly picked up the little tome and hurried after them. A new guardian, thought the little green book, this one certainly has potential, she's gentle and seems to care. She rescued me after all!

Once across the water, the needlewoman made her way purposefully towards the Royal Castle hotel, where she was due to meet an old college friend. As always the bar at this time of day was bustling with people of all sorts of shapes, sizes and ages. With a large glass of wine and a comfortable seat overlooking the wharf, she settled down to wait. Sipping her drink and opening the little book, the young woman began to slowly turn the pages, paying particular attention to the illustrations. The needlewoman had been one of those fortunate people, who had excelled in both the arts and sciences. She had been eager to pursue a career in photography, but her parents had finally persuaded her that a more practical path would be best. As a result after three long tough years she'd qualified as an acupuncturist, a profession which was intensely satisfying, but there was still that lingering desire to do something with those latent, artistic talents. These musings were interrupted by the sound of a rhythmic tapping on the window, glancing up the young woman smiled in delight, her friend had arrived. Disaster struck. Whilst leaping to her feet, the needlewoman sent the wine glass flying. Like a cloudburst, the contents poured down upon the little tome lying directly in its path. Chaos reigned as the girls and staff mopped and wiped the unfortunate victim until finally order was restored. With profuse apologies, and carrying a rather damp LGB, the girls slunk out of the hotel.

Shrugging off the incident in the bar, the pair ambled towards the riverside arm-in-arm, discussing their plans for the next few hours. They were going for a cruise and picnic on the Kingswear Castle, the only remaining coal-fired paddle steamer in the UK. Arriving at their destination and climbing on board, the young women made their way to their seats. LGB, still rather damp from the impromptu soaking, was carefully placed on an adjacent wooden bench and left to dry in the gentle breeze. The women relaxed ready to enjoy the trip. What a magical and soothing experience the voyage proved to be. The weather was idyllic as the boat made its way slowly up the river. The only sound to be heard was the gentle hum of voices, and the churning of the paddles, as they powered their way through the waters of the Dart. The occasional announcement over the loud-speaker failed to detract from the tranquility of the scene. People were in fact, eager to be informed when seals, herons and kingfishers came into view. Finally, as all good things, the excursion came to an end. The needlewoman picked up LGB, who had dried out quite nicely, and the two women reluctantly left the boat. Back on dry land the two friends unenthusiastically parted company promising to keep in touch. The needlewoman, with LGB in tow, made her way back to the B&B where she was staying, her thoughts already focused on the trip back to Hereford the following day.

With the little green book in pride of place on the dashboard, the needlewoman could be seen tearing at great speed up the M5. She was heading home to a party she'd promised to attend, and she was late! Suddenly out of nowhere, with blue lights flashing and sirens screaming, a police car drew up alongside, forcing the vehicle to pull over and stop. The needlewoman was horrified as she came to a halt on the hard shoulder. Meanwhile LGB lay there, pages quaking, terrified by the dreadful din. Fortunately for the young woman, the police officer let her proceed with a dire warning not to offend again and to drive more carefully. As the orange and yellow stripes of the vehicle disappeared into the distance, the young woman and the little book, breathed a huge sigh of relief. As you can imagine the remainder of the journey was undertaken in a far more sedate fashion!

A few hours later, feeling flustered but very relieved, the pair reached home. The journey had taken much longer than the needlewoman had anticipated. She was glad to have avoided a well-deserved ticket, but driving beneath the speed limit had made her later than ever. Dashing into the house, she quickly donned her glad-rags in preparation for the evening's festivities. The pub, where they all planned to meet, was a short drive away and before long she finally drew into the car park. What prompted her to pick up the little green book and take it into the pub, we'll never know, however this fatal decision was to prove the death knell of their relationship. BUT, more of that later!

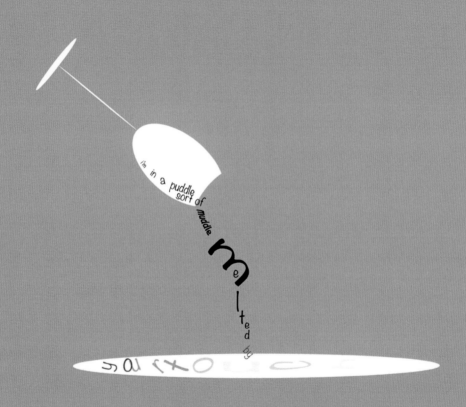

i'm in a puddle
sort of muddle

melted

by

In a puddle sort of muddle,
melted by your touch.

dissolving

the polisher's tale

hollow

When I was young,
I dreamt of lighting up a room,
sweeping a space with
my articulated broom.
I'd heard of passion,
felt it in those songs, that teenage rooms were papered with.

Now I am grown,
I dream of lighting up a face,
sharing a breath with
a pillow like embrace.
I hear of heartbreak,
told in the tunes, that permeate the lonely in hollow, dark, saloons.

Fast forward and visualise the picture inside the pub, a scene of two halves. In one corner, two men smartly but casually dressed, were propped up against the bar deep in conversation. Meanwhile a noisy group of youngsters, dressed to kill, chatted enthusiastically amongst themselves. Suddenly, a pause in conversation announced the belated arrival of the needlewoman, who rushed headlong into the room muttering frantic apologies for her delay. Placing LGB on the edge of the bar and holding centre stage, she proceeded to relate the events of the day, which had been unnerving to say the least. Story complete, the young people began to gather their possessions, impatient for the festivities to begin. As glasses were emptied and pushed willy-nilly onto the bar, the little book, who'd been completely ignored, was gradually forced closer and closer to the edge. From this precarious position LGB was aghast to see the needlewoman disappearing. Please, please don't leave me, whispered the little tome to itself, but as the door slammed shut, the unhappy book slid to the floor in despair.

In a state of shock, LGB lay completely dejected, waiting passively for whatever life had in store. Regardless of what happened next, the little tome really didn't care. In this state of mind it came as no surprise, when a large highly polished brogue placed itself squarely on its front cover.

The owner, rocking backwards and forwards, completely unaware that his size 14 shoes were slowly flattening the book. LGB forced out of its catatonic state began to panic. I'll be squashed to a pulp and of no use to anyone if this continues! This silent plea was instantly answered. The torture stopped and the small tome found itself clasped firmly, and lifted up to rejoin the human race. The owner of the hand, one of the men mentioned earlier, examined the book with interest. My Mother would love this, he thought, and popped the object safely inside his pocket. Glancing at his watch and horrified by what he saw, the polisher bid a hasty farewell and strode out of the pub.

Walking briskly in the deepening gloom, the man knew that he'd pushed his luck this time. He'd just returned from a covert mission with the SAS and had a few days leave, during which he had to nip up to Norwich, before yet another assignment. He'd promised to have a quick pint and that was several hours ago! Reaching his destination he was met, as predicted, by his irate wife. "Where on earth have you been?" she wailed. "You promised me we'd spend the evening together. Just look at the time and you haven't even cleaned your kit yet". Looking extremely sheepish and promising to be as quick as possible, the soldier legged it upstairs to complete his tasks. With boots bulled to within an inch of their life, uniform pressed, the polisher finally threw together a change of clothes for his trip to Norwich. His father had died and the purpose of the visit was to resolve some legal issues that had arisen. Job done, there was one more item to pack, the present for his Mother, namely the little green book. The soldier glanced through it briefly, but books weren't really his thing. If he had any spare time he'd rather watch sport or meet friends in the pub! With the little tome tucked safely away, the polisher hurried downstairs to placate his wife.

The trip from Hereford to Norwich was uneventful but inevitably slow, no direct motorway links to that part of the world. Arriving flustered and with minutes to spare, the polisher hurried into the lawyer's office, to be met by his relieved Mother. She'd been thumbing through some rather dull literature anxiously awaiting his arrival. The thought of the meeting ahead without her son's support had little or no appeal. Expecting to be seen immediately, the pair were surprised to be told that the lawyer was running late. At least this gave them the opportunity to relax, catch up with recent family events, but more to the point, an ideal time for the polisher to deliver his gift. Handing the little book to his Mother, the soldier explained how he'd found it and thought of her. Her reaction was as expected, she was delighted and knew this was a book she'd treasure. LGB, in the past, would have been overjoyed to hear this news but now, with confidence in tatters, the little tome would just wait and see.

Without warning, the door swung open and in walked a stick thin, tall and almost colourless man. Everything about him was grey; his hair, clothes and even the colour of his skin. As he ushered the waiting pair into his office, the polisher's Mother bent down to pick up the little tome. Catching sight of the book, the lawyer's eyes lit up. "Your possessions will be quite safe there," he barked, in a steely voice. Not wishing to argue Mother and son promptly followed the grey man into his chambers. An hour or so later the pair emerged, ashen-faced and silently left the building. As for LGB, there was no sign. All that remained was a selection of magazines, placed in a neat and orderly pile.

the Daily Grind

Tsunamis in Asia, earthquakes in Nepal,
ebola in Africa, we hear about it all.
Disasters served on muesli, one lump or two on line,
news from every angle, espoused in the Daily Grind.
Hedgehogs going awol, badgers being shot,
bees in peril from a virus, ash trees being lopped.
Someone famous had a boob job, (that's supposed to lighten our mood),
someone infamous is lauded, for being very rude.
A general in the election is accused of telling lies,
and comes out in stilettos, no-one is surprised!
Beckham's selling pants, Bill Gates blew his nose,
as the tally of Libyans drowning,
grows and grows and grows.
As they lose their heads in Iraq,
the rest of us lose our minds,
as globally we've forgotten,
the simple power
of being kind.

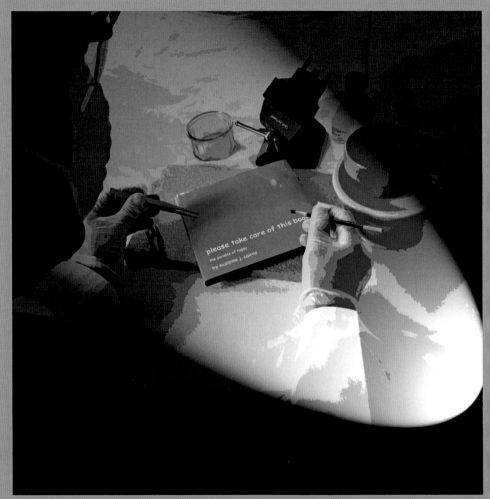

the interrogator's tale

subtle

How swiftly this world changes,
how subtle is the knife,
that slices through our reveries
and
lullabies.

As mother and son left the office, the interrogator began pacing backwards and forwards, becoming more agitated by the minute. Finally he threw open the door and glaring at his unfortunate secretary suggested, that she tidied up and left as quickly as possible. Returning to his inner sanctum he waited impatiently for her to leave. Meanwhile his assistant was diligently performing the task she'd been set. Chairs were placed in regimental lines with precise gaps between each, magazines were arranged in order of size and placed squarely in the middle of every table. Finally her desk was left with not a pen, or even a paper clip, in sight. Checking the end result would meet her employers exacting standards, she gathered her possessions together, wondering as she did so, whether she could bear working for her macabre boss much longer.

The moment the outer door closed the interrogator reappeared, striding to the window he swiftly closed the blinds, isolating the premises from the outside world. With a glance around the room, he quickly straightened the odd chair or two and stalked back from whence he'd come. Moving quietly but purposefully towards the desk, the grey man opened the drawer, removed a key and using his finger tips, carefully withdrew the little green book. With nose screwed up in distaste, he carried the offending object towards a well disguised door, which opened to reveal a most extraordinary world. The room looked vaguely like an operating theatre. A large metal table stood centre stage, above which hung a huge glass lamp, that lit up every nook and cranny. The walls were covered with floor to ceiling shelves, containing books arranged in precise order of size. They were all covered in thick plastic, thus obliterating any sense of their individual identity. However one small space remained, just perfect for LGB. Was this why the little book had been selected, for its size?

The grey man moved towards a large cupboard and removed a tray containing bottles, brushes and other assorted paraphernalia. Donning a white coat and a pair of surgical gloves he proceeded to examine the little tome minutely from front to back, looking for any damage or flaws. Inspection complete, he returned to the tray, selected two of the bottles and gingerly removed their lids. Immediately an overpowering chemical smell pervaded the atmosphere. LGB was absolutely terrified. Picking up a brush, the interrogator set to work. With intense concentration he slowly removed each imperfection, taking particular care to eradicate some rather smudged green writing, and a blurred signature. Finally, the little tome was returned to its original pristine state. Satisfied with the result, the interrogator carefully placed the book onto a roll of plastic. Within moments it was securely wrapped, sealed and yes, placed on the allotted space on the shelf. Clearing away the debris, the grey man cast an eye over his collection, it was complete. He expected to feel elated, having taken years to reach this point, but in fact the reverse was true.

As the days and weeks rolled by, time stood still within the secret chamber and of the grey man there was no sign. Until one day, several months later, the door gradually opened and in strode the interrogator carrying a large metal box and two books. LGB from within his plastic shroud watched intently as the grey man, with great precision, cleansed and wrapped his unfortunate victims. Exercise complete, he stood back thoughtfully surveying the shelves and their contents. Decision reached and choice made, he proceeded to remove two volumes and replace them with his latest conscripts. Moving quickly and deliberately a further ten were withdrawn, including LGB, making a total of twelve in all. The lawyer, with hands trembling, rapidly unwound the tight plastic bindings, replacing them with far lighter restraints. Then taking great care, the tomes were deposited in the steel box and the lid closed. By this time the interrogator was displaying signs of deep distress. With limbs shaking and sweat accumulating on his pallid brow, he lifted the container, switched off the light, left the room and purposefully shut the door. "I must get rid of these quickly," muttered the grey man. With a plan of action mentally in place, the interrogator began to relax and his thoughts turned to the future. The discovery of the little book had proved to be a mixed blessing, the final piece in the jigsaw, completing a collection which had taken many years. The result had left the lawyer facing a huge void in his life, with no sense of purpose. Now, with ten gaps to fill, there was much to look forward to.

Meanwhile LGB lay in its cold dark prison, reflecting on the strange behaviour of the lawyer. People choose books to read but not this odd man, who denied any access to his tomes. Furthermore, when there was no more space on the shelves, some were removed to make way for others. Extraordinary!! Listening intently, the little book strived to make sense of the the muffled voice above. Did the lawyer actually state that this cache of books were to be destroyed? If so, what would that involve? The little green book shuddered. Only time would tell whether LGB's worst fears were to be realised.

just

I just,
wanted to be heard.

Craved for my words,
with subtle springs, to unfurl their wings
and brush the tips of yours.

I just,
wanted to be heard.

Bound and gagged,
in your theatre of the absurd, shackling my verbs,
muffled by your madness.

Now, I'm just,
observed.

the
notegirls'
tale

tar

I feel I know you,
that we've met somewhere before?
But your eyes are unfamiliar,
they're bleak and underscored.
Are these the hands that broke me?
The mouth that spat and choked me,
or is this brush I'm using
plied with tar?

At a book sale in Oxford, tucked out of the way, stood a small table covered in a snowy-white cloth. Lying there twelve books of varying sizes were enclosed in plastic cases, not dense enough to disguise their covers, but clearly there to protect each one. Guarding this assortment of tomes was a tall figure dressed in grey from head to foot, the lawyer from Norfolk. He was obviously there to sell but did little to encourage people to buy; in fact any display of interest was actively discouraged. As time went by the interrogator grudgingly, parted with some of his stock, wincing as would-be purchasers removed the protective covers and flicked through the pages. Some with none too clean fingers. Eventually just three tomes remained, including the little green book, who had been completely overlooked. No-one seems to want me, thought LGB in despair.

Then out of the blue, a pint-sized smiling gentleman approached the table with two very pretty girls in tow, the latter causing a stir, to which they were totally oblivious. The young women were obviously twins and identical too, but their demeanour and attire were poles apart. One, face scowling, was dressed from head to toe in black, with skinny black jeans, black leather jacket and, to complete the outfit, a pair of heavy black boots. The other by contrast clothed in a floaty dress was smiling and trying to chivvy her twin out of her gloomy mood, brought on by their fruitless search for a specific music score. Glancing at the table which they were about to pass, she noticed a strange trio of books, all carefully wrapped. Curiosity aroused, she stopped and picked up the smallest of the three. The grey man hovered anxiously as LGB was removed from its restraint and examined gently by the young woman. "Is this for sale?" she asked. LGB waited with baited breath for the interrogator's response. After what seemed an eternity and with great reluctance, the grey man agreed to the purchase. Thank goodness, thought the little tome, impatient now to leave the cloying smell of plastic behind. Rescue complete, and leaving their Father to browse, the two girls moved on with their minds focused on the search for that elusive manuscript.

Objective achieved, the now smiling twins arrived home where they lived alone with their Father, their Mother having died some years before. As they opened the door two huge black beasts leapt forward to greet them, one in its excitement lunged towards the little book and sent it flying. LGB waited trembling with fear. Based on past experiences nothing good would come from this encounter! Thankfully the swift reaction of the gentler notegirl saved the day. As the little tome was placed out of harms way, the two newfoundlands sank to the floor to wait patiently for their tea!

Dogs fed, the twins could be found seated at a magnificent grand piano, which took pride of place in the centre of a large, light, airy room. The notegirls, both talented musicians, played a wide selection of instruments and performed at venues far and wide. The pair, for once in total harmony, were practicing for a concert which was to take place the following day. The duet they were due to play was tricky, to say the least, and as the girls played on attempting to reach perfection, all sense of time was lost. It was the barking of the dogs, announcing the arrival of their Father, which finally brought them back to earth. Supper hadn't been prepared, let alone cooked!

Eventually, with food eaten and chores completed, the girls settled down to relax; one to watch TV, the other to read the poems within the covers of the little green book. As time drifted by the convivial atmosphere in the room began to change. The 'black twin', tired of being ignored by her sibling and bored by the programmes she'd been watching, began to fume. Finally patience at an end, she leapt to her feet, grabbed the tome from her sisters' hands and flung it across the room. The notegirl, immediately regretting her actions, looked on in horror as LGB landed with a thud against the back of the fireplace. With pages splayed, spine broken and covered in soot and ash, the little green book was a pitiful sight. Rushing to the rescue, and glaring at her sister in the process, LGB was gently removed from the grate and ever so gently cleaned. During the final stages of this demanding task, the notegirl found her thoughts turning to the origins of the tiny tome, wondering who had written it and where it had come from. Searching the book and discovering the information she required, the young woman quickly turned to her laptop, eager to learn more.

With fingers flying across the keys, the girl paused momentarily as her twin joined her eager to make amends. LGB lying close by was intrigued by the girls excitement. What had they unearthed? The twins' search, meanwhile, had revealed the beginnings of a very strange tale. Their little green book had been originally left at Malham Cove in Yorkshire, photographed later at Bolton Abbey and York races, and then apparently had disappeared from the face of the earth. Where it had been since then, only LGB knew. Intrigued by what they'd read, the girls were keen to find out more, and there was one way that they could do that! With a plan of action in place and typing resumed, soon e-mails were flying backwards and forwards through the ether. At last, with business finalised and computer shut down, one notegirl turned and spoke quietly to her twin, "Well, that's that, we're taking the little book home tomorrow."

Overwhelmed by this news, LGB was un-nerved. Thoughts began building and swirling inside its shiny green cover. Feelings of excitement and relief battled with a sense of unease and trepidation. What would the future hold?

Will I really go home tomorrow, agonised the tiny tome, and if I get there will my shelf still fit? It would be a long, harrowing night for LGB before these questions could be answered.

an epilogue

Authors are motivated to write books for a myriad of reasons, but one desire unites us all, and that is the hope that someone will read our scribblings. In September 2014, having completed a small offering of poetry and photographs about the rise and tortuous demise of a love affair, I recognised that the heart and soul of a writer was encapsulated in their work, and there was a clear parallel between the custodianship that authors craved from their readers, and the kindness that all individuals yearn for from their relationships.

Fresh off the press in a pristine, but simple, shiny green jacket 'please take care of this book', was laid on my behalf on a limestone escarpment, high in the Yorkshire Dales. In many ways it was an odd experiment, but one that might just highlight the fact that humans are essentially kind, compassionate and generous. In a disposable world, where death, disease and disaster are fed to us intravenously by the media., I hoped to prove that sensitivity and kindness still live in our landscapes.

My little book was to be sacrificed, but only in the belief that its words might connect people in a positive way and that finally, its adventures would bring it back to the shelf where it all began. As the months passed sporadic sightings and photographs were posted to social media, but then everything went disappointingly quiet.

It seemed that my idealism was näive and I was destined to write another book about the heavy burden of loss. Then almost a year later, out of the blue, a phone call from an enthusiastic, bubbly and slightly apologetic young woman, explained that she had rescued LGB from a book sale in Oxford.

Fate dictated that I was out when a small brown package was posted through my letterbox, so I never had the chance to say thank you to the young heroine, in person . However, the small green tome, a little worse for wear like all survivors, sits proudly with its buddies on my shelf. A tiny optimistic beacon with its own raft of experiences which, perhaps one day, an author will take the time to write down.   sjc

soup

Are books just a soup of syllables,
some random black on white,
a zebra like compendium to keep
you warm at night?
Or are these libraries bodyguards,
maps to happiness,
charts of paths well travelled
that make us ravenous . . .

to connect?

p.s.

the travels of a small book

I t is remarkable how far a small book can travel in the course of a year. LGB certainly covered a significant amount of territory during its twelve steps home. Travelling by car, rail, ferry, horse-drawn cart and even by air, the tiny tome connected people throughout the UK and even extended its reach to Hong Kong.

It seems that we are not only linked by the people we encounter, but by the books that we choose to read. Who knows, perhaps one day you might just come across a small square green book, with a slightly dog-eared cover, and your story will also become part of this plot?

the twelve steps

1. Malham Cove
2. Bolton Abbey
3. York Races
4. Stow on the Wold
5. London
6. Brighton
7. Hong Kong
8. Dartmouth
9. Hereford
10. Norwich
11. Oxford
12. Lambourn

the authors

In many ways Suzanne J. Cairns is an enigma wrapped up in a conundrum, with a multitude of coloured strings to her bow. Carrying a wordy degree in her back pocket, she has written in many guises, exhibited her paintings, been involved in several building projects and has a love of interior design. Currently, she lives in the Berkshire Downs with a dog called Wellie and a Buddhist cat called Garlic.

Having completed '*please take care of this book*', the unique opportunity arose for Suzanne to write the second in the series with someone else. This was a dangerous project from the start, for authors are notoriously solitary and egotistical, but a shared goal, shared genes and a shared sense of humour, meant it all went surprisingly well.

Elizabeth J. Saunders also has an eclectic CV which ranges from school teacher married to the airforce, to equestrian enthusiast with a love for restoring properties. She currently lives in rural Devon with two newfoundlands called Gully and George and an athletic spouse, redefining the concept of retirement as they seek to tame an acre of woodland.

(Oh and in case you are wondering, Liz played with her words on the white pages of this book, whilst Suzi had a penchant for anything that was green!)

Please feel free
to share your photographs
of the little green book
on its website or Facebook page

books in this series

please take care of this book
- the parable of topsy

please take care of this book too
- twelve steps home

please take care of this book 111
- tripping on a rainbow

for further information
www.pleasetakecareofthisbook.com